Founding Editor: John Milne

The Macmillan Readers provide a choice of enjoyable reading materials for learners of English. The series is published at six levels – Starter, Beginner, Elementary, Pre-intermediate, Intermediate and Upper.

Level control
Information, structure and vocabulary are controlled to suit the students' ability at each level.

The number of words at each level:

Starter	about 300 basic words
Beginner	about 600 basic words
Elementary	about 1100 basic words
Pre-intermediate	about 1400 basic words
Intermediate	about 1600 basic words
Upper	about 2200 basic words

Vocabulary
Some difficult words and phrases in this book are important for understanding the story. Some of these words are explained in the story and some are shown in the pictures. From Pre-intermediate level upwards, words are marked with a number like this: ...[3]. These words are explained in the Glossary at the end of the book.

Contents

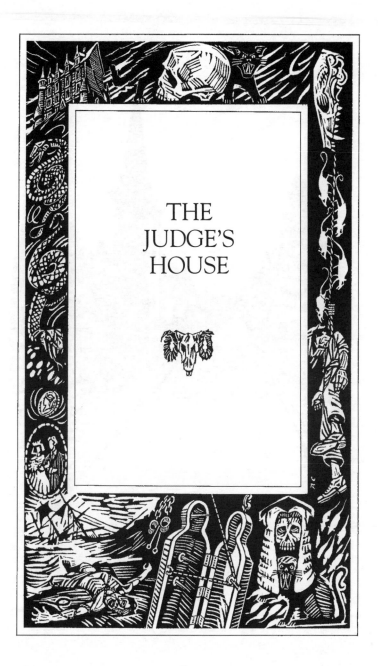

THE JUDGE'S HOUSE

He took a train to a small quiet town called Benchurch.

THE
JUDGE'S HOUSE

Malcolm Malcolmson was a student at college. Malcolm was twenty-one and he was in his final year. Classes had finished and Malcolm was studying hard for his examinations. But Malcolm was unable to study at home. He lived with his family and the large house was always noisy.

'I can't study here at home,' Malcolm told his father. 'It's far too noisy. I'm going to find a quiet house in a small country town. I'll be alone there and I'll be able to work hard.'

His father agreed and Malcolm packed all his books and papers into a suitcase. He took a train to a small quiet town called Benchurch. Benchurch is in the country. Malcolm had never been there before.

Malcolm stayed the first night in a small hotel. The next morning, after breakfast, he walked round the town. In the quietest part of the town, Malcolm found a large, old house. The garden in front of the house was very untidy and the house looked empty. There was a shop not very far from the house. Malcolm went into the shop and asked about the old house.

'Does anyone live in that old house down the street?' Malcolm asked the man in the shop.

'The house is empty,' replied the man. 'No one has lived there for many years. Go to the lawyer in the High Street. He knows about the house. He'll be able to help you.'

Malcolm walked back to the High Street. The lawyer's

office was near the hotel. Malcolm went into the office and met the lawyer.

'That house has been empty for many, many years,' the lawyer told him. 'There is a story about the house. People say strange things about it. No one wants to live there.'

'I am a student,' Malcolm replied. 'I want to study hard and I'm not worried about stories. I like that old house and I want to live there. It's very quiet and I'll be able to work hard at my studies.'

Malcolm gave the lawyer enough money to rent the house for a month. The lawyer handed him the keys to the house. Malcolm took the keys and walked back to the hotel. He packed his suitcase and got ready to leave.

'I'm leaving now,' he told the woman who owned the hotel.

'Are you leaving the town?' the woman asked him.

'No,' replied Malcolm, 'I'm going to stay here, in Benchurch. I have found an old house. It's very quiet and I'll be able to work hard there.

The woman asked him about the house. When Malcolm told her, she looked frightened.

'You can't live there,' she said. 'You can't live in that house. That's the Judge's House.'

'Why are you so afraid?' Malcolm asked her. 'What is wrong with the Judge's House? Tell me about it.'

'A famous judge lived there a long time ago,' the woman explained. 'He was a very cruel man. He had no mercy on any criminal. He ordered the criminals to be hanged. Many people died because he showed them no mercy.'

The woman's face was white. She was very, very afraid. But Malcolm was busy thinking about his examinations. He did not notice the woman's fear.

'Don't worry about me,' he told her. 'I have my work to do. I'll be very busy. I have a lot of studying to do and many books to read. I won't have any time to be afraid of stories.'

Malcolm said goodbye to the owner of the hotel. She looked very unhappy, but she did not say any more. Malcolm picked up his suitcase and walked from the hotel to the Judge's House.

Malcolm unlocked the door and went inside. The rooms were very dark. Malcolm pulled aside the dark, heavy curtains. The furniture in the rooms was old. It was all covered with sheets. The dining room was big and there was a large table in the centre. Malcolm decided to live in that one room.

I'll work in this room and I'll eat and sleep here, he said to himself. I do not need any of the other rooms.

He moved the chairs in the dining-room to one side. He

carried a bed from a bedroom and put it beside a wall. He lit a fire and put his books on the big table. He started studying and worked until the evening. In the evening, he prepared some supper. After supper, it was beginning to get dark. The daylight was fading. Malcolm lit a lamp and put some more wood on the fire. Then he sat down again at the table and continued studying.

He worked until eleven o'clock. Then he stopped and made a pot of tea. He put some more wood on the fire. Outside the light of the lamp and the light of the fire, the room was very dark. There were dark shadows on the walls and behind the chairs. But Malcolm was happy. He was working hard.

I can work really hard here, he said to himself. I'll do well in the examinations.

There was an old wooden chair beside the fire. The chair had a high back and it looked comfortable. Malcolm sat down in this chair and drank his tea. At first, the house was very quiet. There was no noise in the room at all. But then Malcolm heard a noise. He listened carefully. The noise was getting louder.

Rats, said Malcolm to himself. The light from the fire and from my lamp frightened them away at first. Now they have become used to the light. They are no longer afraid. They have come to look at me. They want to know who I am.

The rats were everywhere. They were running across the floor and over the furniture. Malcolm heard them running under the wooden floor beneath his feet. They ran in and out of holes in the walls. They squeaked and they scratched.

Malcolm was not afraid. Rats did not frighten him. He finished drinking his tea. Then he got up and picked up the lamp. He walked round the room. He lifted the lamp high and looked at the walls. There were some old paintings hanging on the walls. The paintings were covered with dirt and dust. Malcolm was unable to see them clearly. The rats were watching him. He saw their bright eyes shining in the lamplight. When he came too near them, the rats ran quickly away.

Then Malcolm saw something very strange. There was a rope hanging beside the old wooden, high-backed chair. The rope hung from the ceiling between the fire and the chair. The rope was fixed to a big alarm bell on the roof of the house. If anyone pulled the rope, the alarm bell rang.

Malcolm went back to the fire and sat down on the chair. He drank another cup of tea. Then he went back to the big table and read some more books. The noise of the rats continued, but he did not notice it.

Malcolm sat reading for hour after hour. Suddenly he

looked up from his books. Something had happened. He listened carefully. The rats had stopped their noise. There was complete silence in the room. Malcolm looked at the fire. He had forgotten to put more wood on and the fire was almost out. Then Malcolm felt a sudden, cold shiver running through his body.

Malcolm looked at the high-backed chair by the fire. Something was sitting on the chair. It was an enormous rat. Malcolm had never seen such a large rat in his life. It was looking at Malcolm and it did not move. Malcolm picked up a book from the table. He raised his arm and threw the book at the rat but the rat did not move. It opened its mouth and showed its big, sharp teeth. Its gleaming red eyes looked cruel in the lamplight.

Malcolm stood up quickly. As soon as he stood up, the rat moved. It jumped from the chair to the rope of the alarm-bell. It ran up the rope and disappeared into the darkness. Immediately, the other rats came back again. They came out of the holes in the walls. The room was once more filled with the noise of their squeaking and scratching.

Malcolm looked at his watch. It was nearly morning. He lay down on the bed and fell asleep. When he woke up again, the sun was shining through the windows.

Malcolm got up and had some breakfast. Then he went out for a long walk. He took his books and some bread and cheese with him. It was a beautiful day and the sun was shining brightly. Malcolm felt happy. He walked through the fields and then he sat down and read his books. At lunchtime, he ate the bread and cheese. He sat reading all through the afternoon.

In the early evening, he came back to the Judge's House. He heard the rats as soon as he opened the door. They were already running about and making a noise. Malcolm lit a fire and made his supper. After supper, he sat down in the big chair by the fire and smoked a cigarette. Then he sat down at the big table and went back to work.

That night, from the very beginning, the rats were not afraid of Malcolm. They ran up and down the room – over and under every piece of furniture. They watched Malcolm out of the holes in the walls. Their little, bright eyes shone in the lamplight. But they did not trouble Malcolm. He became used to them. From time to time, he looked up from his books and watched them playing their games.

Malcolm worked for hour after hour. Suddenly he looked up from his books. Once again, there was silence in the room. It was exactly like the night before. The noise of the rats had stopped completely. There, on the high-backed chair beside the fire, sat the same enormous rat. The rat looked at Malcolm with its evil eyes.

Malcolm quickly picked up a book and threw it at the rat. The book did not hit the rat and the rat did not move. Malcolm stood up and moved towards the rat. The rat ran up the rope in the same way as the night before. As soon as it had disappeared, all the other rats started to squeak and scratch. Malcolm looked at his watch. It was midnight.

I'll have another cup of tea, he said to himself. Then I'll get back to my books.

Malcolm put some more wood on the fire and made another pot of tea. He sat down again in the high-backed chair. He drank the tea and smoked a cigarette. Then he looked at the alarm bell rope. He reached out and touched the rope. He lifted up the end of the rope and held it in both hands. It was strong, but it also felt soft and smooth.

Malcolm had an idea. He thought of a plan to kill the enormous rat. He lifted up the end of the rope and put it on the table. Then he piled up some books and put them near him on the table.

Now I am ready for the rat, he thought to himself. When it comes again, I'll see the rope move. And I'll have these books to throw at it. This time I'll hit the rat and kill it.

Malcolm began his studies once again. He worked for about half an hour. Suddenly the rats stopped the noise. The room was silent. He looked up and saw the enormous rat. It was climbing down the rope. It jumped from the rope onto the high-backed chair. It sat on the chair and looked straight at Malcolm.

Malcolm picked up the first book on the pile. He threw it at the rat. The rat moved a little and the book did not hit it. Malcolm threw a second book, then a third and a fourth. This last book hit the rat. It gave a loud squeak. Then it ran up the back of the chair, jumped onto the rope and climbed up quickly. Malcolm watched the rat in the lamplight. It climbed up and came near one of the big paintings on the wall. Then it jumped from the rope to the painting. The rat disappeared into a hole in this painting. Malcolm looked at the painting carefully. He wanted to remember it.

I'll have a good look at that painting in the morning, he thought to himself. I'll be able to see it more clearly in the daylight.

It was now very late. Malcolm went to bed and slept well. The next morning, he woke up and felt happy. It was another sunny day.

Good, he thought to himself. I'll get out again for a long walk. I'll read my books in the open air.

While Malcolm was drinking a cup of tea, a woman came to the house. She was the cleaning woman. She had come to dust and clean the house.

'I'm going out for a long walk,' Malcolm told the woman. 'You can clean the house while I am out.'

Before he left the house, Malcolm spoke again to the woman. He pointed up at the painting on the wall. It was the one with the hole in the corner. The enormous rat had disappeared into this hole.

'Please clean this painting very carefully,' Malcolm asked the woman. 'I want to see it clearly.'

Then Malcolm left the house. Again he walked through the fields. After some time, he sat down and read more and more. He worked very hard. In the afternoon, the weather changed. The sun went behind some black clouds and it became windy.

I'll go back to the Judge's House now, thought Malcolm. It's going to rain.

On his way back, Malcolm came to the small hotel. He decided to go in. He wanted to talk to someone. There was a man sitting in a chair in the sitting–room. The man introduced himself to Malcolm.

'Good evening,' he said. 'I am the doctor in this town. And I know who you are. You are the student who is living in the Judge's House. Are you happy there?'

'I am able to study hard in the house,' replied Malcolm. 'That is the most important thing for me. I am studying for my final examinations.'

'And nothing troubles you in the house?' asked the doctor.

'There are hundreds of rats in the house,' replied Malcolm. 'But they do not trouble me very much. I am not afraid of rats. However, there is one enormous rat,' added Malcolm. 'It sits on a chair and looks at me with evil eyes. I want to kill this big rat.'

Malcolm told the doctor all about the enormous rat. He described the high-backed chair and the rope of the alarm bell.

'Does the rat always come down and go up that rope?' asked the doctor.

'Always,' replied Malcolm.

'Do you know what that rope is?'

'It's a very strong and a very soft rope,' replied Malcolm. 'But I don't know anything more about it.'

The doctor looked at Malcolm for a few moments. Then he spoke quietly and slowly.

'When the judge was alive, he was very cruel. He condemned many criminals to death. That was the rope that the hangman used. The hangman made a noose at the end of the rope. The noose was put over the criminal's head. Then the criminal was hanged by the rope until he was dead. The rope by the fire is the hangman's rope.'

Malcolm and the doctor talked about the Judge's House for about an hour. Then Malcolm walked back to the house.

The weather had now changed completely. It had become cold and a strong wind was blowing. When he was inside the house, Malcolm heard the wind blowing round it.

The cleaning woman had lit the fire and Malcolm put on some more wood. He had some supper. Then he went and sat down at the big table. It was time to get back to his studies once again. Before he started reading his books, he looked round the room. He noticed the rope hanging between the high-backed chair and the fireplace. He thought about the doctor's story. This was the rope used by the hangman. Many men had died with this rope round their necks.

Malcolm stood up and walked over to the rope. He took. it in his hands. While he was holding the rope, he felt it move. He looked up and saw the enormous rat. It was climbing slowly down the rope. The rat suddenly saw Malcolm. It turned round and ran quickly up and disappeared into the hole in the painting. All the other rats immediately began running around again, squeaking and scratching.

Malcolm picked up the lamp and walked towards the high-backed chair. He stood behind the chair and held the lamp high above his head. He looked at the painting. The cleaning woman had worked hard. She had cleaned off all the dust and dirt from the painting. Malcolm was able to see the hole in the corner where the rat disappeared.

Suddenly Malcolm felt terribly afraid. His face went white. He now saw that it was a painting of a judge in his robes. The judge's face was cruel and his eyes were evil. The eyes of the judge were like the eyes of the enormous rat.

Malcolm held the lamp higher. Now he was able to see the whole painting. In the painting, the judge was sitting in a wooden, high-backed chair. The big chair was beside a fireplace. A rope was hanging down between the chair and the fireplace. It was a long rope and in the painting it looked strong and soft.

Malcolm understood. It was a painting of the room in which he was standing. The wooden, high-backed chair was the same. The fireplace was the same. The strong, soft rope was the same.

Malcolm looked round the room. He looked at the fireplace and then at the rope. Then he looked at the chair. He gave a loud cry. The lamp almost fell from his hand.

The enormous rat was sitting in the chair. The rope was hanging down behind it. The rat's eyes were staring at Malcolm. They were the same eyes as the judge's in the painting.

Inside the room, everything was completely silent. Outside, the wind was blowing strongly. The wind made Malcolm remember the town outside the house.

I am becoming foolish, Malcolm said to himself. I must forget about the doctor's story. I will go back to my books and study hard. I must be strong or I will go mad. I must stop thinking about the judge and the hangman's rope.

Malcolm looked again at the chair. The enormous rat was no longer there. It had disappeared. Malcolm sat down again at the table and began to study. He worked for about an hour. As usual, the other rats ran round the room over and under the furniture. Malcolm listened to their squeaking and scratching. Then suddenly, the noise stopped. Malcolm listened. The room was silent. The rats had disappeared. But outside, the wind was blowing more and more strongly. The rain was beating against the windows Malcolm looked at the fire. It was nearly out. The room was cold.

I must put more wood on the fire, he said to himself.

He stood up and suddenly he stopped. He had heard a noise in the room. It was a very quiet scratching noise. Malcolm looked round the room. He saw nothing. Then he looked up at the hangman's rope.

Malcolm was horrified. In the dim light of the lamp, Malcolm saw the enormous rat. It was holding on to the rope. It was about halfway between the high ceiling and the floor. And it was biting at the rope with its sharp, cruel teeth. It was slowly biting through the rope.

Malcolm watched in horror. As he watched, the rat went on biting the rope. Suddenly the bottom half of the rope fell on to the floor. The rat had bitten right through it.

Now the rat was holding on to the top end of the rope. Malcolm picked up a book and threw it at the rat. The book nearly hit the rat. The rat dropped from the rope and landed on the floor. Then it ran away into the darkest corner of the room.

Malcolm was now terribly afraid.

If I am in trouble, I will not be able to ring the alarm bell, he thought to himself. If anything happens to me, I will not be able to call for help.

Malcolm sat down at the table, but he was not able to read his books. The room was still silent. He looked up again at the painting. He shut his eyes and rubbed them. Then he looked at the painting once again.

'It can't be true,' he shouted out loudly in the empty room.

He looked at the painting. The fireplace and the rope

were still there. And the high–backed chair was in the painting too. But the high–backed chair in the painting was empty. There was no one sitting in it. The judge in the painting had disappeared.

Malcolm slowly moved his eyes from the chair in the painting to the real chair in the room. His heart stopped beating for a few moments. His whole body felt like ice. The judge was sitting in the big, wooden high-backed chair.

The judge's eyes were evil and his mouth was cruel. His eyes were looking straight at Malcolm. A clock somewhere in the house struck twelve. It was midnight. Slowly the judge stood up and picked up the rope from the floor. He held the soft, strong rope in his hands. Slowly he twisted the rope into a noose. He started to walk towards Malcolm.

The judge came slowly nearer. Malcolm moved backwards. Suddenly the judge tried to throw the noose over Malcolm's head. Malcolm moved his head to one side. The noose missed Malcolm and the rope fell to the floor.

The judge slowly pulled the rope back. He picked it up. Once again, the noose was in his hands.

Suddenly Malcolm heard a noise. It was the alarm bell on the roof of the house. It was beginning to ring. But it was not ringing loudly. Malcolm looked up. The end of the rope which was hanging from the high ceiling was covered with rats. More and more rats were coming out of a hole in the ceiling. They were climbing down the rope. The rats were trying to help Malcolm. They were trying to make the alarm bell ring. But it was not yet ringing loudly.

The judge heard the alarm bell. His face twisted with anger. He came nearer to Malcolm. His eyes were looking straight at Malcolm. Malcolm's body felt like ice. He was unable to move. The judge slowly came up to Malcolm. He

21

put the noose over Malcolm's head and round his neck. He pulled the noose tighter and tighter.

The judge carried Malcolm to the–high backed chair. He stood Malcolm on the chair. Then the judge disappeared. The enormous rat suddenly appeared once again. The rat picked up the end of the rope on the floor. It ran up the wall holding the rope with its teeth. It jumped from the wall to the other end of the rope. The rats on the top end of the rope fled away in terror. They disappeared through the hole in the ceiling.

The enormous rat tied the two ends of the rope together. Then it jumped from the rope to the painting. It disappeared into the hole in the corner of the painting.

The judge appeared once again. He stood beside Malcolm. Malcolm was now standing on the chair with the noose tightly round his neck. The rope went from Malcolm's neck right up to the ceiling. The judge knocked the chair away from under Malcolm's feet. Malcolm's body swung from the end of the rope. The alarm bell began to ring. It rang louder and louder.

The alarm bell rang out loudly over the small town of Benchurch. The noise woke the people up. They came running to the Judge's House. They knocked loudly on the door. But no one opened it. Then they knocked the door down and went into the house.

They found Malcolm in the dining-room. His body was hanging from the end of the alarm bell rope. A man pointed up at the painting on the wall. It had not been cleaned for many years. For the first time, they were able to see the painting clearly.

'Look,' the man cried. 'It's a painting of the judge.'

They all stood and looked at the painting. The judge in the painting was sitting in the big, wooden high-backed chair beside the fire. There was a smile on the judge's face. It was an evil smile.

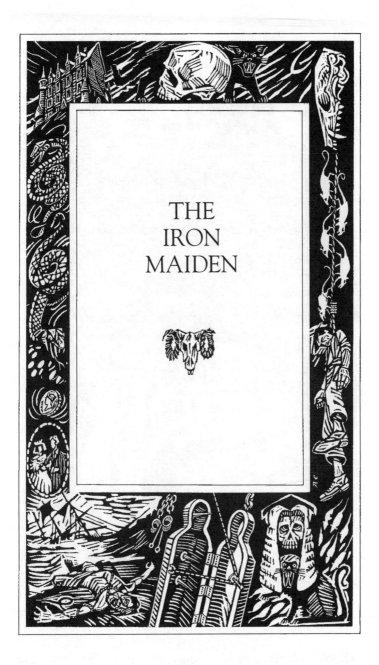

THE
IRON
MAIDEN

The oldest building in Nürnberg is the castle. The castle stands high above the centre of the city.

THE IRON MAIDEN

This is a story of horror. It happened many years ago, but I still remember it clearly. I will never forget it – and my wife will never forget it either.

After we were married, my wife, Amelia, and I went to Germany. We went to stay in the old city of Nürnberg.

In Nürnberg, Amelia and I met an American. Like us, he was on holiday. His name was Elias. The three of us became good friends and we spent a lot of time together. Every day, we went round the city looking at the buildings. They were very old and very beautiful.

The oldest building in Nürnberg is the castle. The castle stands high above the centre of the city. From the castle, visitors can look down and see the city below them. There is a moat at the foot of the castle walls. At one time, the moat was filled with water. The moat kept the people in the castle safe from their enemies.

Now, however, there is no water. There has not been water in the moat for hundreds of years. Today, there are fruit trees and beautiful gardens in the moat. The road up to the castle is steep and long.

One day, Amelia, Elias and I went to visit the castle. We walked up the steep road and looked down at the gardens in the moat far below. It was summer and the sun was hot. People were sitting in the shade under the trees in the gardens. It was a beautiful scene.

We walked further up the hill and looked down again into the moat. Far down, near the bottom of the wall, we saw a cat. It was a large black cat and she was playing with her kitten. The kitten was chasing its mother's tail and they were happy together. It made us feel happy too.

'How happy they are!' said Elias. 'Let's join them in their game. We can play with them.'

Elias bent down and picked up a stone.

'Look,' he said, 'I'll drop this stone. It will fall near the kitten. And it won't know where the stone came from. It will puzzle the cats.'

'Be careful,' said Amelia. She looked unhappy and frightened. 'Please be careful. Don't hit the little kitten with the stone.'

'I won't hit the kitten,' replied Elias. 'I want to play with them. I don't want to hurt them.'

'But it's a long way down,' said Amelia. 'It's dangerous.'

'No, no,' said Elias. 'Look, I'll drop the stone far away from the kitten and its mother.'

Elias bent over the wall. He opened his hand and dropped the stone. We all looked down. The stone fell and

hit the kitten. The kitten died immediately.

The mother cat looked up. Her green eyes stared straight at us. Then she looked at her dead kitten and licked its body. She looked up at Elias again. She opened her mouth and showed her sharp teeth. Her teeth were red with the kitten's blood.

Suddenly the cat tried to run up the wall. She wanted to reach us. She ran up a short way and then fell back to the ground. She fell on top of the kitten. Her fur became red with the kitten's blood. The cat looked very frightening.

Amelia was so upset that she felt ill. I took her to a nearby seat. She sat down in the warm sun.

I walked back to the wall. Elias was standing there. He was looking over the wall. The cat was still trying to run up. She wanted to reach us. Every time she tried to climb up, she fell to the ground again. She looked more horrible every time.

'The poor cat is going mad,' said Elias. 'It was an accident. I'm sorry I dropped that stone. I only wanted to play with the cats. I didn't want to kill the pretty little kitten.'

Amelia felt better after a few moments. She walked back to us. We all looked over the wall again. The cat looked up at us. She saw Elias and tried to run up the wall once more.

'Oh, the poor cat!' cried out Amelia. 'She's so angry. She wants to get near you, Elias, and kill you.'

Elias laughed when Amelia said this. He was a brave man. He was not afraid of a cat. A cat could not hurt him. The cat heard Elias laugh. Immediately she stopped looking at us and went to sit down beside her dead kitten. She began again to lick the blood from its body.

We left that part of the wall and walked on towards the castle. From time to time, we stopped and looked down over the wall. Every time we looked down, we saw the cat looking at us. She was following us. She was walking round the bottom of the wall. At first, she was holding her dead kitten in her mouth. Then she took the kitten and hid it somewhere. She followed us by herself.

We went on up the road. We came to a big gate. From the gate, a path led to the castle. There is a very famous building in the grounds of the castle. This building is called the Torture Tower. The Torture Tower is the most interesting building in the city of Nürnberg.

We went into the Tower. We were the only visitors there. A man was sitting by the door. He was a guide. His job was to show visitors round the Tower.

The Tower was very dark inside. The only light came through the door. We began to climb up the dusty, wooden stairs. At the top of the stairs, there was a large room.

There were a few small windows in the walls of this room. In the light from the windows, we saw the things in the room more clearly. There were large swords on the walls. These swords were so big that they had to be held with two hands. On the floor, there were bloodstained blocks of wood. Hundreds of years ago, people's heads were cut off on these blocks of wood with an axe.

Everywhere there were horrible instruments. These instruments were used long ago to torture people. Some of the chairs had sharp spikes on their seats. People were hurt when they sat down on them. There were iron collars to put round people's necks. There were things that looked like baskets. But they were made of steel. A basket was put over a person's head and the head was crushed very slowly.

All these things were horrible and frightening to look at. Amelia's face went white and she held my hand.

In the centre of the room, there was the most frightening thing of all. This was called the Iron Maiden. It was made of metal and was shaped like a woman. It was covered with dust and was very dirty. It was very old, too. On the front of the metal body there was a ring made of iron. There was a rope on the ring. The other end of the rope went through a pulley on a wooden pillar in the room.

The guide showed us this Iron Maiden. He pulled the rope and the front part of the metal body opened up. It was like a heavy door on a hinge. We looked inside the body. There was room inside for a person to get in and stand up straight. The door was very heavy. When the guide let go of the rope, the door fell quickly and shut tightly.

We looked at the inside of the door more carefully. It was

31

In the centre of the room, there was the most frightening thing of all. This was called the Iron Maiden.

very frightening! On the inside of the door, there were long iron spikes. These spikes had sharp points at the ends. When the door was shut, some of the spikes went through the eyes of the man inside. Other spikes went through his heart and his stomach.

Amelia saw these spikes. She was so frightened that she fainted. I carried her downstairs and out into the sun again. I sat with her. Soon she felt better. We then went back and found Elias. He was still looking carefully at the Iron Maiden.

'I want to get inside that,' Elias said. 'I want to see what it feels like to stand inside. But first you must tie my hands together and then my feet.' Elias spoke with great excitement. 'We must find some rope,' he said to us.

Elias spoke to the guide, 'Bring me some rope.'

The guide did not answer. He did not move. He only shook his head. Elias took some money from his pocket. He offered it to the guide.

'Here. Take this money,' Elias said to him. 'And don't be afraid.'

The guide took the money. Then he found a piece of rope. He came back and tied the rope round Elias' hands.

Then Elias said, 'Wait a moment. Don't tie my feet together now. I'm a heavy man and you won't be able to lift me into the Iron Maiden. I will get inside. Then you can tie my feet together when I am in.'

While he was talking to us, Elias got inside the Iron Maiden. It was just big enough. There was no room left in it. Amelia looked frightened, but she said nothing.

The guide tied Elias' feet together with the rope. Now Elias could not move at all. Both his arms and his feet were tied tightly together. Elias was very happy and he smiled at Amelia.

'That's good,' he laughed. 'Now close the door very slowly.'

'Oh, no! No! No!' cried Amelia. 'I can't watch you. I can't!'

Elias looked at Amelia and then at me.

'Take Amelia outside,' he said. 'She's afraid. Take her for a walk.'

Amelia did not move. She held my arm tightly and she trembled with fright.

Slowly, very slowly, the guide let the rope go through the pulley. The door closed little by little. The spikes got nearer Elias' face and body. He looked happier and happier as they got nearer and nearer.

After a few minutes, the guide had let the door down only a short way. I looked at Amelia. Her lips were white. She was not looking at Elias. She was staring at the ground near the bottom of the Iron Maiden. I looked too. The black cat was sitting there. The cat's eyes were shining. There was still blood on her fur.

I cried out, 'Look! There's the cat.'

The cat stood up. She looked very fierce.

Elias saw the cat and laughed.

'Has the cat followed us here?' he laughed. 'If she comes near me, kick her with your foot. I can't move.'

Just then, Amelia fainted. I put my arm round her shoulders to hold her up.

At the same time, the black cat gave a loud cry. She jumped up quickly. She did not jump towards Elias. She jumped at the guide. She scratched his face with her long, sharp claws. Her claws went into the guide's eyes and down his cheeks. His cheeks were badly torn.

The guide screamed. He jumped back and let go of the rope in his hands. The rope ran through the pulley. Elias saw the rope slipping past him quickly. For a second, he

35

looked terrified. His eyes stared straight ahead. His lips moved, but no sound came from them. The door fell and shut tight.

I pulled open the door. When I opened the door, the spikes came out of his body and Elias fell onto the ground. His face looked awful.

I hurried to Amelia. I took her outside and put her on the seat in the fresh air. I did not want her to see Elias' body. It looked very, very horrible.

I then ran back into the room. The black cat was sitting near Elias' head. She was purring loudly and was licking the blood on Elias' face.

Quickly I walked over to one of the walls and took a big sword in my hands. With all my strength, I raised the sword above my head and let it fall suddenly.

I was right to kill the cat. I am sure of that. No one can say that I was cruel.

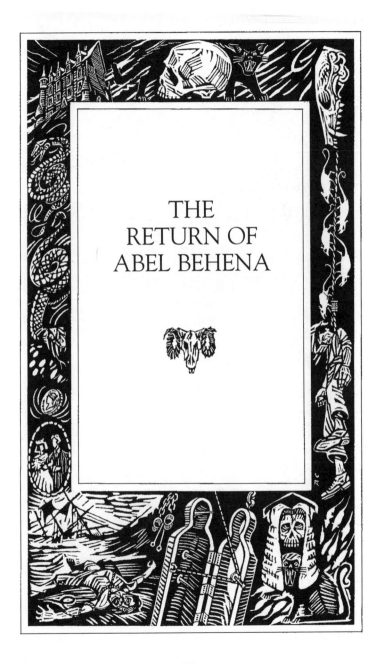

THE
RETURN OF
ABEL BEHENA

The cliffs rose up steeply above the sea and above the small town.

THE RETURN OF ABEL BEHENA

Two young men once lived in a small town beside the sea. The town was in the south-west of England, on the coast. There was a harbour in the town. Every day, ships and fishermen's boats sailed in and out of the harbour.

On each side of the harbour, there were high cliffs. The cliffs rose up steeply above the sea and above the small town. Over many, many years, enormous rocks had fallen from the cliffs into the sea. These rocks lay half in and half out of the water. They were very dangerous for the ships and for the fishermen's boats. Sometimes, when there was a storm, the wind blew the boats against the rocks. Then the boats were wrecked. Sometimes, the fishermen were drowned.

The two young men in this story were fishermen. Their names were Abel Behena and Eric Sanson. Abel and Eric were friends. They had been friends since they were children. Abel and Eric were both the same age – twenty years old. They were the same height and they looked very much like each other. The only big difference between them was the colour of their hair. Abel had dark, black hair. Eric had light, fair hair.

Eric lived in a small cottage on the cliffs. Abel lived quite near, in another cottage. They both saw the sea every day of their lives. They saw the sea when the weather was fine. Then the sea was smooth and calm and beautiful. They saw the sea when the weather was stormy. Then the sea was rough and cruel and ugly.

One day, when they were both fourteen, Abel saved Eric's life. The two boys had gone out fishing early one morning. They sailed out of the harbour in a small boat. The weather was fine and the sun was shining. The sea was calm. But the weather changed later in the day. It became stormy and the sea became rough. The boys tried to sail their boat back to the harbour. But the strong wind blew against their boat. It blew their boat towards the huge rocks.

The wind blew their boat against one of the rocks. Abel jumped from the boat onto the rock. He held on tightly with one hand. He held a long, strong rope in his other hand. The boat sank and Eric was not able to jump. He tried to swim through the rough water to the rock. But the strong wind was blowing him out to sea.

Abel threw one end of the rope towards Eric. Eric caught the end of the rope and held it tightly. Abel slowly pulled him towards the rock. Eric reached the rock and Abel pulled him to safety. Abel had saved Eric's life.

After this, their friendship grew stronger. They were always with each other. They worked together and they played together. But, at the age of twenty, their friendship was broken. They both fell in love at the same time— unfortunately, they both fell in love with the same girl.

The girl's name was Sarah. Sarah lived in a small house in the town. The house was on the edge of the town below the cliffs. Sarah lived in the house with her mother. Sarah liked Abel and she liked Eric. She wanted to marry one of them. But she did not know which one.

One day, Abel and Eric both came to Sarah's house. They both asked her the same question.

'Do you love me?' asked Abel. 'Will you marry me?'

'Do you love me?' asked Eric. 'Will you marry me?'

'I want to marry one of you,' Sarah replied. 'But I don't know which one. I love you, Abel. I love you, Eric.'

'But you must decide between us,' the two men said together. 'You must choose one of us.'

'Wait until my birthday,' said Sarah. 'I will be eighteen on 11th April. I will tell you my decision on my birthday.'

On 11th April, early in the morning, both men came again to Sarah's house. They stood outside the house waiting for her. Sarah did not know what to do. She was unable to decide between the two young men. She loved them both. Sarah's mother was busy in the kitchen. Sarah asked her mother for advice.

'What shall I do?' she said to her mother. 'I love Abel Behena. I love Eric Sanson. Which one shall I marry? They are waiting outside. What shall I tell them?'

Sarah's mother thought quietly for a few moments. Then she spoke to Sarah.

'Go out by the back door and take a walk along the cliffs,' she said. 'I will talk to the two men.'

'But what will you say to them?' asked Sarah.

'I will tell you later,' her mother replied. 'Both men want to marry you. But only one of them can marry you. Both men are poor. Neither of them has enough money to get married. But I have an idea. You go for a walk and I will talk to them.'

Sarah went out of the house by the back door. The two men did not see her. She went for a walk along the cliffs. Her mother opened the front door and spoke to Abel and to Eric.

'You are waiting for my daughter,' she said to the two men. 'Both of you want to marry her. She has to decide between you. What are we going to do?'

'Has she made her decision yet?' asked the two men.

'She is unable to decide,' replied Sarah's mother. 'She loves you, Abel Behena. She loves you, Eric Sanson. She is unable to choose between you. But I have an idea.'

'Tell us your idea,' the men said.

'You are both poor,' said Sarah's mother. 'Neither of you

has enough money to get married. But why not put your money together? Then one of you will have enough money to marry my daughter.'

'What do you mean?' asked Abel.

'I don't understand you,' said Eric.

'Listen,' said Sarah's mother. 'I'll explain. You must toss a coin for my daughter. The one who wins the toss will marry her. But before you toss the coin, you must make an agreement.'

'An agreement!' said the two men in surprise. 'What kind of agreement?'

'Before you toss the coin, you must agree to put your money together,' replied Sarah's mother. 'The winner will take all the money. He will buy goods with the money and sell the goods in foreign countries. When he is rich, he will return. Then he will be able to marry my daughter.'

Sarah's mother went back into the house. She left the two men standing outside.

When I win the toss, thought Abel, I'll sail to foreign countries. When I return, I will be rich and I will marry Sarah.

When I win, thought Eric, I'll sail to foreign countries. I will be rich when I come back and I will marry Sarah.

Neither of the men thought about losing. They both thought of winning. Sarah came back from her walk.

'I must talk to you both,' she said. 'I promised to give you my decision today. But I cannot decide. I cannot choose between you. I do not know what to do.'

'Stop worrying about the matter,' said Abel. 'Your mother has solved the problem for us.'

'We are going to toss a coin,' Eric explained. 'The one who wins the toss will marry you.'

'And we have made an agreement,' added Abel. 'We are going to pool our money together. The winner will take all the money. He will sail to foreign countries and use the money to trade. He will then become rich. When he returns, he will marry you.'

'That's our agreement,' said Eric.

'Today, 11th April, is my birthday,' said Sarah, with a laugh. 'I am eighteen today. On my next birthday, I will be nineteen. The man who wins must come back on my nineteenth birthday. On 11th April next year I will marry the man who wins.'

'We agree,' both men said.

'Here's a coin,' Abel said to Eric. 'Take it and toss it.'

Eric tossed the coin in the air. He caught it with both hands. He held the coin on the back of one hand and hid it with the other hand.

'Heads or tails?' Eric asked Abel. 'Take your choice.'

'I choose heads,' said Abel. 'Heads.'

Eric slowly lifted his hand from the coin. The three of them looked at the coin. It was lying on the back of Eric's hand. They were looking at the head of the king on the coin. Abel had chosen correctly. Abel was the winner.

Abel shouted out happily. He had won. He took Sarah and held her in his arms.

Eric was very disappointed. He had lost. He threw the coin angrily out into the sea. It sank below the water.

'Don't be angry,' Abel said to Eric. 'Let us be friends. Sarah will be my wife and I will make her happy. You will be like a brother to both of us.'

'I won't. I won't,' Eric cried out angrily. 'You have one year, Abel Behena. You must be back here on 11th April next year. That is the date of the wedding. If you are not back on that day, I will marry Sarah.'

'I will return in one year,' replied Abel. 'I will return in time for the wedding.'

Abel turned and spoke to Sarah.

'You will wait for me, won't you?' he asked her. 'You won't marry Eric before I return, will you?'

'I promise to wait for you,' replied Sarah. 'I will wait for you for one year. I won't marry before 11th April next year.'

Abel tried to make friends again with Eric.

'Don't be angry, Eric,' he said. 'We have been friends all our lives. Please let us stay friends.'

'You are not my friend any more,' Eric replied angrily. 'I hope you don't come back. I hope the Devil takes you!'

Eric Sanson walked away angrily. He did not say goodbye. Abel stayed and talked to Sarah.

Early the following morning, Abel was awakened suddenly by a noise. Someone was outside his cottage. Abel

45

got up, went to the door and opened it. Eric Sanson was walking away quickly. His back was turned to Abel. Then Abel saw a small bag lying on the ground in front of the door. Eric's money was in the bag. Also, there was a note, tied to the bag.

Take this money and go. I will stay here. But remember – you have to be back here on 11th April next year, or I will marry Sarah.
Eric Sanson

Abel took Eric's money and put it with his own. He bought a lot of toys with the money.

'I will take these toys with me on a ship,' Abel told Sarah. 'And I will sell them in foreign countries. I will become rich. When I return, I will have enough money to marry you.'

On the day of his departure, Abel said goodbye to Sarah. He promised to write to her.

'But remember I will be busy,' he told her. 'Also, letters

will take a long time to come to you from foreign countries. But don't forget your promise. Wait for me.'

'I will wait for you until 11th April next year,' Sarah promised. 'I will not marry anyone before that day.'

Abel left on a ship at the end of April. He waved goodbye to Sarah from the ship as it left the harbour.

———

Sarah waited for a letter from Abel. She woke early every morning hoping for a letter. But no letter came. The months passed – May, June, July – but there was no letter for Sarah. At first, Sarah waited patiently. But, as the time passed, she became more and more unhappy.

'Perhaps he has forgotten me,' she thought. 'Perhaps he will never come back.'

Then, one morning in August, she received a letter. In the letter Abel wrote:

I am doing very well in business. I have already sold half of the toys. Soon I will sell them all. When I have sold them, I will start on my return journey. Do not forget me. I love you. Our wedding will take place on the day of my return.

Again the months passed and no other letters came from Abel. Soon it was January of the following year. Sarah again became unhappy. She began to see Eric Sanson every day. Eric asked her the same question many times.

'Will you marry me?' he said. 'Perhaps Abel Behena will never come back. He has a lot of money now. Perhaps he has forgotten you.'

Sarah's reply was the same every time.

'Wait until 11th April,' she said. 'If Abel is not here on 11th April, then I will marry you.'

January and February passed. And then it was March. Sarah had not received another letter from Abel. She saw Eric every day and she began to forget Abel. Eric asked her the same question again and again.

'Will you marry me?' he asked.

'It is the month of March now,' replied Sarah. 'It is April next month. Abel has not written another letter. And he has not come back.'

'He will never come back,' said Eric.

'I will marry you on my birthday,' Sarah said. 'I will marry you on 11th April.'

So Eric and Sarah agreed to get married on 11th April. Sarah started to make her wedding-dress. It was soon the beginning of April. The eleventh of April was getting nearer and nearer. And no letter came to Sarah from Abel Behena.

'He will not return,' Sarah said to herself. 'On 11th April, I will marry Eric Sanson.'

———

One night, in the first week of April, there was a terrible storm. The wind blew and the sea became rough. The men of the town walked down to the harbour. They looked at the sea. The wind was blowing stronger and the sea was becoming rougher and rougher.

Lightning flashed in the sky. Suddenly, in a flash of lightning, the men saw a ship. The ship was trying to reach the harbour. But the strong wind was blowing it towards the rocks. The men watched in horror. The wind grew stronger and blew the ship against a rock. There was a great crash and the ship sank quickly into the sea.

The men of the town ran from the harbour along the

shore. They ran towards the rocks. They heard the cries of the people in the water. They were shouting for help. The people were trying to swim towards the shore. But the strong wind was pulling them out to sea.

'I'm going to help them,' Eric Sanson shouted to his friends. 'I'm going onto that huge rock. Then I can climb down on the other side. If anyone gets near that rock, I will be able to save them.'

'Don't try to climb onto that rock,' his friends said to him. 'The wind will blow you into the sea and you will be drowned.'

'I know that huge rock,' he shouted to them. 'Abel Behena saved my life there when we were boys. I will be able to save anyone who comes near that rock.'

Eric climbed carefully onto the wet rock. He was holding a long, strong rope in one hand. He climbed up onto the top of the rock. Then he climbed slowly and carefully down the other side. The men on the shore were no longer able to see Eric. He was hidden behind the huge rock.

Eric stood staring out into the black, rough water. Suddenly, he heard a cry. Someone was trying to swim to the rock. The lightning flashed. Eric saw a man's head in the water. Eric shouted loudly and the man heard him. Eric threw the rope towards the man. The man caught it and tied it round his body.

Eric began to pull the rope towards him. The man was coming nearer and nearer to the rock.

Then the lightning flashed again. Eric, for the first time, saw the man's face clearly. It was the face of Abel Behena.

Abel Behena had returned. He had come back to marry Sarah. Sunday, 11th April was a few days away. Eric wanted to marry Sarah on that day. Now Abel Behena had returned.

49

Eric stood staring out into the black, rough water.

Abel will marry Sarah on 11th April, Eric thought angrily to himself. What shall I do? I will never love anyone else but Sarah.

In the same flash of lightning, Abel had seen Eric's face.

'It's my old friend, Eric Sanson,' he thought to himself.

Abel smiled. Eric saw the smile on Abel's face. He felt a strong hatred and anger growing inside him.

'No,' he shouted out loud. 'You will not come back. I will marry Sarah.'

Eric let go of the rope. It fell onto the rock and then slipped into the water. Abel sank in the sea. The wind and the waves pulled him away from the rock.

Eric stood for a few moments in horror. He remembered the smile on Abel's face. Abel had been happy to see him again. But Eric had not saved Abel's life. He had let Abel drown in the sea.

Eric hurried back over the top of the huge rock. He climbed back down to the shore. The men were waiting for him.

'Did anyone come near the rock?' the men asked. 'We heard a man crying for help.'

'He did not come near me,' replied Eric. 'No one came near the rock. I waited, but no one came.'

One of the men held a lamp up to Eric's face.

'What is wrong with you?' the man asked. 'Have you seen a ghost? Your face is white and you are shaking with fear.'

'I slipped and nearly fell into the water,' Eric explained. 'The rope fell from my hand. It fell into the water.'

Eric remembered Abel's face again with horror.

'I can never tell them the truth,' he thought to himself. 'Abel Behena saved my life there on that rock. Now, in the same place, I have let my friend drown in the sea.'

'No one came near the rock,' he told the men again. 'I

did not hear anyone crying out for help. I did not see anyone.'

Eric hurried back home and went to bed. But he was not able to sleep. When he closed his eyes, he saw once again the face of Abel Behena. Abel was in the water and there was a smile on his face.

The next morning, Monday morning, the storm had gone completely. The sky was clear and the sun was shining brightly. The wind had dropped and had become soft and gentle. Eric stayed at home all day. He remembered the face of Abel Behena. Eric was afraid.

But, in the evening, he felt much braver.

Abel Behena has gone now for ever, he told himself. He will never return. Next Sunday is 11th April. It is Sarah's birthday. And it will be our wedding-day. Abel will never come back to marry Sarah.

Eric went to Sarah's house. He wanted to see her and talk about the wedding. Sarah was busy making her wedding–dress when Eric came to the house.

'Have you not finished making the dress yet?' Eric asked with a laugh. 'You must hurry up. It will soon be Sunday and we are getting married on Sunday.'

'I have not forgotten,' replied Sarah. 'Sunday is my birthday and it will be my wedding-day. But who will I marry? Perhaps Abel will come back before Sunday.'

Eric became angry and left the house. He walked back to his cottage on the cliffs. But he was not able to look at the sea. He was now afraid of the sea. Abel Behena had drowned in the sea with a smile on his face.

The days passed slowly. Eric became brave again and went to see Sarah every day. Tuesday came and went. Wednesday came and went. Then it was Thursday.

On Thursday evening, Eric was sitting in his cottage. He was thinking about Sunday – his wedding-day. A man from the town came to the cottage. He was a friend of Eric's and he wanted to speak to him. The man looked very sad and unhappy.

'I want to speak to you about the ship that was sunk in the storm,' the man began. 'I've heard some news about it. I've heard the names of the passengers. They were all drowned. Some of the bodies were washed up on the shore. But not all of them. They are still looking for some of them. One body of a man has not been found. He was a passenger on the ship. He was a friend of yours.'

'A friend of mine? Who was he?' Eric asked.

'I'm sorry, very sorry,' the man replied. 'I have bad news for you. One of the passengers on that ship was Abel Behena. He was on his way back home.'

Eric's face went white. He gave a loud cry. Then he held his head in his hands.

'I'm sorry,' said the man again. 'It is very bad news for you. Abel Behena was your best friend. He once saved your life. But you were not able to save his life. You climbed over that dangerous rock. But you were not able to save him. No one was saved that night. The sea was too rough and too cruel.'

Eric sat silent with his head in his hands. His whole body was shaking.

'I'm sorry,' the man repeated once again. Then he went out of the cottage and left Eric alone.

———

Friday was a quiet day. Nothing unusual happened in the small town. Eric became brave once again. He went to see Sarah.

'One more day,' he said to her. 'On Sunday we will be married.'

'Yes,' said Sarah. 'We will be married on Sunday if Abel does not come back.'

Something unusual happened in the town on Saturday afternoon. Some children were playing round the harbour. The tide was high and the harbour was full of water. The children saw something strange floating in the water. They ran into the streets of the town. They shouted loudly to everyone.

'Come quickly!' they shouted. 'There's a big fish in the harbour.'

Men and women ran quickly to the harbour. They stood round the harbour and looked at the water. But they saw nothing unusual.

'What did you see?' a man asked the children.

'A big fish with a long tail,' a young boy answered.

'It was an enormous fish,' said another boy. 'And it had a long, long tail.'

'The tail went down into the water,' added a girl. 'We were not able to see the end of it.'

The men and women stood on the harbour wall for some time. The tide was now going out and the harbour was not so full of water. They looked into the harbour, but they saw nothing.

'The tide will have taken anything strange in the harbour out to sea again.'

They did not tell the children why they were so interested. They were still looking for bodies from the wrecked ship. When a person is drowned, the body sinks at first to the bottom of the sea. Then, after five or six days, it comes up again to the top and floats on the water. Perhaps the children had seen the body of one of the passengers from the ship.

The men and women waited for more than an hour. The tide went out and the harbour was almost empty of water. But they saw nothing. They decided to go home.

'It's getting late now,' they said to each other. 'There will be another high tide in the night. Perhaps we will find it on the shore at low tide tomorrow morning.'

'What about the long tail?' one man asked. 'The children said it had a long, long tail.'

'A children's story,' said a woman. 'Children like to make up stories. Now it's time to go home and go to bed.'

Then it was Sunday – the day of the wedding. The weather was fine. The sun was shining and the sky was clear. Eric got up very early in the morning. He got dressed in his wedding clothes.

'This is my wedding-day,' he said to himself. 'Abel Behena cannot take Sarah from me now. He cannot come back – alive or dead.'

The church bells began to ring. It was time for the wedding. Eric left his cottage and walked towards the church. He looked at the sea for a few moments. Then he quickly turned his eyes away. But he noticed that the tide was going out.

When Eric arrived at the church, he stood at the door. He waited for Sarah. All their friends were inside the church. Sarah came up the path. She was wearing a beautiful white wedding–dress. Eric took her hand and they walked into the church together. The church bells stopped ringing. The wedding-service had begun.

They walked out of the church hand in hand. Now they were married. They were man and wife.

They walked together towards Sarah's house in the town.

There was a body lying on the shore.

Sarah's mother was preparing the wedding meal for them there. All their friends walked behind them. They walked slowly and happily down from the church to the shore. Then they walked along the edge of the shore towards the town.

Suddenly, Sarah gave a cry. She pointed at the shore. Everyone stopped and looked. There was a body lying on the shore. Its head was lifted up against a rock. And its eyes seemed to be looking straight at Eric and Sarah.

Some men ran down to look at the body. There was a rope tied round its middle.

'The tail,' said one of the men. 'The children talked about a long tail. It was this rope.'

They looked more carefully at the body. Then a man turned and shouted to everyone.

'It's Abel!' he shouted. 'It's Abel Behena.'

Sarah looked at Eric in horror. She did not move. Abel had promised to return. This was the return of Abel Behena. He had come back on the wedding-day.

Eric said some words quietly to himself. Sarah fainted and fell to the ground. Some friends carried her to her mother's house.

'The Devil helped you,' Eric said. 'The Devil took you. And the Devil brought you back.'

Points for Understanding

THE JUDGE'S HOUSE

1 Why did Malcolm Malcolmson want to go to a quiet country town?
2 In the quietest part of the town, Malcolm found a large, old house.
    (a)   What did the lawyer tell Malcolm about the old house?
    (b)   What did Malcolm say to the lawyer?
3 What did the woman who owned the hotel tell Malcolm about the old house?
4 Malcolm decided to live, work and sleep in one room in the old house.
    (a)   What room did he decide to live in?
    (b)   Where did he put his books to start studying?
5 Where did Malcolm sit to drink his tea?
6 But then Malcolm heard a noise. The noise was getting louder. What was making the noise?
7 What did Malcolm notice between the old high-backed chair and the fire?
8 Suddenly the other rats were silent. What was sitting in the high-backed chair?
9 Where did Malcolm go to study the next day?
10 It was exactly like the night before. What happened on the second night of Malcolm's stay in the house?
11 Malcolm reached out and touched the rope. What was the rope like?
12 What did Malcolm ask the cleaning woman to do very carefully?
13 What did the doctor tell Malcolm about the rope of the alarm bell?
14 Malcolm held the lamp high above his head and looked at the painting.
    (a)   Who was the person in the painting?
    (b)   Where was he sitting?
    (c)   What was hanging between the chair and the fireplace in the painting?
    (d)   What did Malcolm suddenly understand?

15 Later that night, Malcolm heard a very quiet scratching noise, What
    was the enormous rat doing?
16 Malcolm looked up at the painting once again. 'It can't be true,' he
    shouted.
    (a)   What did he notice about the painting?
    (b)   What was sitting in the real chair in the room?
17 The alarm bell was beginning to ring. How were the other rats
    trying to help Malcolm?
18 The alarm bell rang out loudly over the small town of Benchurch.
    What did the people find when they knocked the door down and
    went inside the house?

THE IRON MAIDEN

1 The storyteller and his wife met an American.
    (a)   Where were they visiting in Germany?
    (b)   What was the American's name?
2 The oldest building in Nürnberg is the castle. What was there at the
    foot of the castle walls?
3 Elias opened his hand and dropped the stone.
    (a)   Why did Elias want to drop the stone?
    (b)   What happened when he dropped the stone?
4 The three friends walked up towards the castle. What did the
    mother cat do?
5 What was the name of the famous building in the castle?
6 What happened when someone was put inside the Iron Maiden?
7 'I want to get inside that,' Elias said.
    (a)   Why did Elias want to get into the Iron Maiden?
    (b)   What did he ask the guide to do to his hands and feet?
8 What happened to the guide when he was slowly lowering the rope?
9 I was right to kill the cat.
    (a)   What did the storyteller do to the cat?
    (b)   Do you think he was right?

THE RETURN OF ABEL BEHENA

1 On each side of the harbour, there were high cliffs.
    (a)   What had fallen from the high cliffs?
    (b)   What sometimes happened when there was a storm?

2 How did Abel save Eric's life when they were both fourteen?
3 But, at the age of twenty, their friendship was broken. What happened when Eric and Abel were twenty?
4 'I will tell you my decision on my birthday,' Sarah told the two young men.
   (a) What decision did Sarah have to make?
   (b) When was her birthday?
5 Sarah's mother had an idea.
   (a) What did Sarah's mother tell Abel and Eric?
   (b) What agreement did Abel and Eric have to make?
6 'I hope the Devil takes you!' Eric said to Abel.
   (a) Why was Eric angry?
   (b) What will happen if Abel does not come back on 11th April next year?
   (c) Does Eric want Abel to come back?
7 The months passed, but there was no letter for Sarah.
   (a) What did Sarah think when no letters came from Abel?
   (b) When did she receive a letter?
   (c) How many letters did she receive?
8 Eric asked Sarah many times to marry him. When did she agree to marry him?
9 One night, in the first week of April, there was a terrible storm.
   (a) What happened to the ship in the storm?
   (b) Where did Eric run to?
   (c) Who did Eric see at the end of the rope?
   (d) What did Eric do?
10 What did the children see in the harbour on Saturday afternoon?
11 What did Eric notice about the sea when he was walking to the church?
12 Suddenly Sarah gave a cry. She pointed at the shore.
   (a) What did Sarah see on the shore?
   (b) What was tied round its middle?
   (c) Who was it?
13 Eric said some words quietly to himself. Sarah fainted and fell to the ground. What did Eric say?

Exercises

The Judge's House

True or False?

Read the story outline. then look at the sentences below. Write T (True), F (False) or ? (Don't Know).

Malcolm Malcomson was a twenty-one-year-old student. He was preparing for his final examinations at college and he wanted to study in a quiet place. He wanted to be alone.

The Judge's House had been empty for a long time. Malcolm rented the house and lived in one room. There was a painting of the judge on the wall of the dining room. A rope hung from the ceiling.

Rats ran around the house at night. Malcolm was not afraid of them, but he disliked the big rat that sat on the chair by the fire.

1 | T | Malcolm Malcomson was a student.

2 | | He had been a student for twenty-one years.

3 | | He was near the end of his college studies.

4 | | He needed a quiet place to study.

5 | | He wanted to live in a house with quiet people.

6 | | No one had lived in the Judge's House for a long time.

7 | | Malcolm paid money to live in the house.

8 | | He used all the rooms in the house.

9 | | There was a painting on the wall of the dining room.

10 | | The painting hung from a rope.

11 | | Malcolm was afraid of rats.

12 | | The big rat sometimes slept on the chair by the fire.

Making Sentences

Write questions for the answers.

1 *Why did Malcolm rent the old house?*
   He rented the old house because it was quiet.

2 *Who*
   The man in the picture was the old judge.

3 *What*
   Malcolm heard the sound of rats at night.

4 *Where*
   He studied in the dining room.

5 *How*
   He read at night by the light of a lamp.

6 *What*

   The hotel owner said that the old judge was a cruel man.

7 *How many*
   There were many rats in the house.

8 *Did*
   No, the rats did not eat Malcolm Malcolmson.

9 *When*
   The judge appeared at midnight.

10 *Where ...*
   The people found Malcolm's body in the dining room.

63

The Iron Maiden

Comprehension

Read the story outline. Then answer the questions.

Nürnberg is in southern Germany. In English, the name of the city is Nuremberg. The man who tells the story went there in the late nineteenth century. He and his wife met an American called Elias.

They visited the castle together. The castle was the oldest building in Nürnberg. At the castle, Elias threw a stone and killed a kitten by accident.

The castle had a famous tower – the Torture Tower. Many people were killed in this tower during the sixteenth century. One instrument of torture was the Iron Maiden. This was a box with sharp metal spikes inside.

Elias wanted to stand in the box. He enjoyed being frightened. He asked the guide to shut the door very slowly. But the kitten's mother jumped at the guide. He let go of the door and it shut tight. Elias was killed.

1   In which country does the story take place?

....

2   What was the oldest building in the city of Nürnberg?

....

3   What happened when Elias threw the stone?

....

4   In which century were many people killed in the Torture Tower?

....

....

5   What was the Iron Maiden?

....

6 Why did Elias want to stand inside the Iron Maiden?

....

7 Why did the guide let go of the door?

....

8 What happened to Elias?

....

Place Names

In English, the spelling of some countries and cities is different from the original languages.

Write the English spelling from the box next to each city below.

> Venice   Nuremberg   Moscow   Cairo   Cologne
> Athens   Seoul   Munich   Bombay   Prague

1	Nürnberg	*Nuremberg*
2	München	
3	Köln	
4	Venezia	
5	Athina	
6	Praha	
7	Sŏul	
8	Moskva	
9	El Qâhira	
10	Mumbai	

Word Focus: *like*

You can use *like* with a noun (*He likes sport*), with the infinitive form of a verb (*He likes to play sport*) or with a verb + *-ing* (*He likes playing sport*).

Write full sentences using *like* with the infinitive and with the verb + *-ing*.

1 Elias / liked / be frightened

Elias liked to be frightened.

Elias liked being frightened.

2 Amelia and her husband / liked / look at old buildings

3 I / don't like / work too hard

4 He / likes / listen to loud music

5 They / like / eat foreign food

Words From the Story

Read the sentences. Then write each word in bold next to the correct meaning below.

1 Ships and boats sailed in and out of the **harbour**.
2 On each side of the harbour, **cliffs** rose steeply above the sea.
3 There were huge **rocks** at the foot of the cliffs.
4 Sometimes the wind blew ships onto the rocks and the ships were **wrecked**.
5 Many fishermen were **drowned**.
6 Eric lived in a small **cottage**.
7 Eric **tossed** a coin into the air. 'Heads or tails,' he called.
8 Abel was trying to swim towards the **shore**.
9 Eric **let go of** the rope and Abel sank back into the sea.
10 A few days later Abel's body was **washed up** on the shore.

a _rocks_ .... large hard stones in the ground or on the coast

b .... a small house in the country

c .... killed in water – unable to breathe air

d .... very badly damaged; beyond repair; destroyed; sunk

e .... the high steep sides of hills by the sea

f .... brought to land by wind or tide

g .... stopped holding something (phrasal verb)

h .... the land on the edge of a sea, lake or river

i .... threw something lightly or casually into the air

j .... a place where boats or ships can stay safely

Dictionary: notes on words

harbour	The US spelling is *harbor*. A large harbour is called a *port*.
wrecked	*Wreck* has a silent 'w' like *write* and *wrong*. Planes, trains and cars *crash*, ships are *wrecked*.
cottage	In the nineteenth century, when this story was written, a *cottage* was often a small house for poor people such as fishermen; it had one or two rooms. Now, in the twenty-first century, a *cottage* is a small but expensive house in the country, often used at weekends or for holidays only.
toss	You rarely *toss* something to someone: the verb *throw* is more common.
heads or tails	English coins always have the *head* of the king or queen on one side; the other side of the coin is called the *tail*.
be washed up	You can be *washed up* on a desert island, but you *wash up* the dishes in the kitchen.

The Return of Abel Behena

Story Outline

Complete the gaps. Use each word or phrase in the box once.

> body   fishermen   money   towards   help   marry   countries
> birthday   rich   poor   return   washed up   days   planned
> week   town   wrecked   rope   pulled   let go of   men

Two young [1]......*men*...... lived in a small fishing [2]................................ .
They were both [3].. and they were
[4]... . Their names were Eric Sanson and Abel
Behena.

Both of them wanted to [5].. Sarah, but
Sarah's mother said that they were too poor to marry her daughter.
'But, if you put your money together, one of you will have enough
money to marry Sarah.'

They agreed to put their 6.. together and

toss a coin. The winner would marry Sarah. Sarah said, 'I will marry

the man who wins on 11th April next year. I will marry one of you in

one year on my nineteenth 7.. '

Eric tossed a coin. 'Heads or tails?' he asked Abel. Abel won. He took

Eric's money, and said, 'I'll sail to foreign 8... .

When I get back, I will be 9... and I will marry

Sarah. I will 10... on 11th April.'

'I hope the Devil takes you,' said Eric Sanson.

Nearly a year later, Abel had not returned. Eric 11....................................

to marry Sarah on 11th April. Then, a few 12....................................

before the wedding, a ship was 13.................................... on the rocks.

Eric and the villagers tried to 14.. the

people on the ship. Eric threw a 15.. to a

drowning man and 16... him

17.. the shore. The man was Abel

Behena. Eric saw his face and 18............................. ....

the rope.

The next 19.. Eric married Sarah. As they

came out of the church, they noticed a body 20......................................

.... on the beach. The dead body seemed to stare at Eric and Sarah.

It was the 21... of Abel Behena.

Time Expressions with *in*

> In English, we often use '*in*' with time expressions to talk about future events:
> *We'll get married in a year. / We'll get married in a year's time.*
> *We'll get married a year from today.*

Rewrite the sentences using *in* with the correct time expression.

1   Today is 11th April. I will come back on 11th April next year.
    I will come back in a year. / in a year's time.
    ....

2   The doctor said: 'Come back one week from today.'
    She said:
    ....

3   The shop assistant said: 'It's one o'clock now. Your photos will be
    ready at four o'clock.'
    He said:
    ....

4   Today is Tuesday. The new supermarket will open on Thursday.
    The new supermarket
    ....

5   It's June. My sister is going to go on holiday in September.
    My sister is
    ....

Dates and Times

Complete the gaps with *in, at* or *on*.

1 ...*in*... April   2 .... Friday   3 .... 9th September

4 .... the year 2020 5 .... midnight   6 .... lunchtime

7 .... the morning   8 .... a minute   9 .... 23.30

Time expressions with ago

In English, we often use ago to talk about past events and show how recently they happened.
I went to Japan four years ago.

Rewrite the sentences using *ago* with the correct time expression.

1   It's 9.30. The train left at 9.25.
    The train left five minutes ago.
    ....

2   It's Friday today. I posted the letter on Monday.
    I posted
    ....

3   She left school in the year 2000.
    She left
    ....

4   I haven't seen him for six months.
    I last saw him
    ....

5   Miss Corder has worked here for a year.
    Miss Corder started
    ....

6   We moved to a new apartment in January this year.
    We moved
    ....

7   This book is more than fifty years old.
    This book was written
    ....

8   This year is my parents' twentieth wedding anniversary.
    My parents got married
    ....

9   The first European settlers went to North America in the early seventeenth century.
    The first European settlers went
    ....
    ....

Published by Macmillan Heinemann ELT
Between Towns Road, Oxford OX4 3PP
Macmillan Heinemann ELT is an imprint of
Macmillan Publishers Limited
Companies and representatives throughout the world
Heinemann is a registered trademark of Harcourt Education, used under licence.

ISBN 978 0 2300 3514 0
ISBN 978 1 4050 7664 7 (with CD pack)

This retold version by John Davey for Macmillan Readers
First published 1983
Text © John Davey 1983, 1992, 2002, 2005
Design and illustration © Macmillan Publishers Limited 2002, 2005

This edition first published 2005

Illustrated by Paul Compton and Wendy Hall
Original cover template design by Jackie Hill
Cover photography by Zefa

Printed in Thailand
2010 2009 2008
5   4   3   2   1

with CD pack
2010 2009 2008
10 9 8 7 6